20 CLASSIC HITS
Playalong *for* Flute
GOLD EDITION

WISE PUBLICATIONS
London/New York/Paris/Sydney/Copenhagen/Madrid/Tokyo

Exclusive Distributors:
Music Sales Limited
8/9 Frith Street, London W1V 5TZ, England.
Music Sales Pty Limited
120 Rothschild Avenue, Rosebery, NSW 2018, Australia.

Order No. AM960718
ISBN 0-7119-7839-5
This book © Copyright 1999 by Wise Publications.

Music arranged by Paul Honey and Jack Long.
Music processed by Enigma Music Production Services.
Cover photography by George Taylor.

CDs produced by Paul Honey.
Instrumental solos by John Whelan.
Engineered by Kester Sims.

Your Guarantee of Quality:
As publishers, we strive to produce every book to the highest commercial
standards. This book has been carefully designed to minimise awkward page
turns and to make playing from it a real pleasure.
Particular care has been given to specifying acid-free, neutral-sized paper
made from pulps which have not been elemental chlorine bleached. This pulp
is from farmed sustainable forests and was produced with special regard for
the environment.
Throughout, the printing and binding have been planned to ensure a sturdy,
attractive publication which should give years of enjoyment. If your copy fails
to meet our high standards, please inform us and we will gladly replace it.

Music Sales' complete catalogue describes thousands of
titles and is available in full colour sections by subject,
direct from Music Sales Limited.
Please state your areas of interest and send a
cheque/postal order for £1.50 for postage to:
Music Sales Limited, Newmarket Road, Bury St. Edmunds, Suffolk IP33 3YB.

www.musicsales.com

Guest Spot

Fingering Guide 4

A Whiter Shade Of Pale 6
Procol Harum

A Whole New World 8
From Walt Disney Pictures' 'Aladdin'

Bridge Over Troubled Water 12
Simon & Garfunkel

Don't Cry For Me Argentina 20
From 'Evita'

He Ain't Heavy... He's My Brother 15
The Hollies

Here, There And Everywhere 18
The Beatles

I Dreamed A Dream 26
From 'Les Misérables'

I Know Him So Well 23
From 'Chess'

Imagine 28
John Lennon

Lady Madonna 30
The Beatles

Moon River 33
From 'Breakfast At Tiffany's'

Mull Of Kintyre 41
Wings

Nights In White Satin 36
The Moody Blues

She Loves You 38
The Beatles

Unchained Melody 44
The Righteous Brothers

Up Where We Belong 46
From 'An Officer And A Gentleman'

Where Do I Begin 48
Theme from 'Love Story'

Words 54
Boyzone

Yesterday 50
The Beatles

You Must Love Me 52
From 'Evita'

Fingering Guide

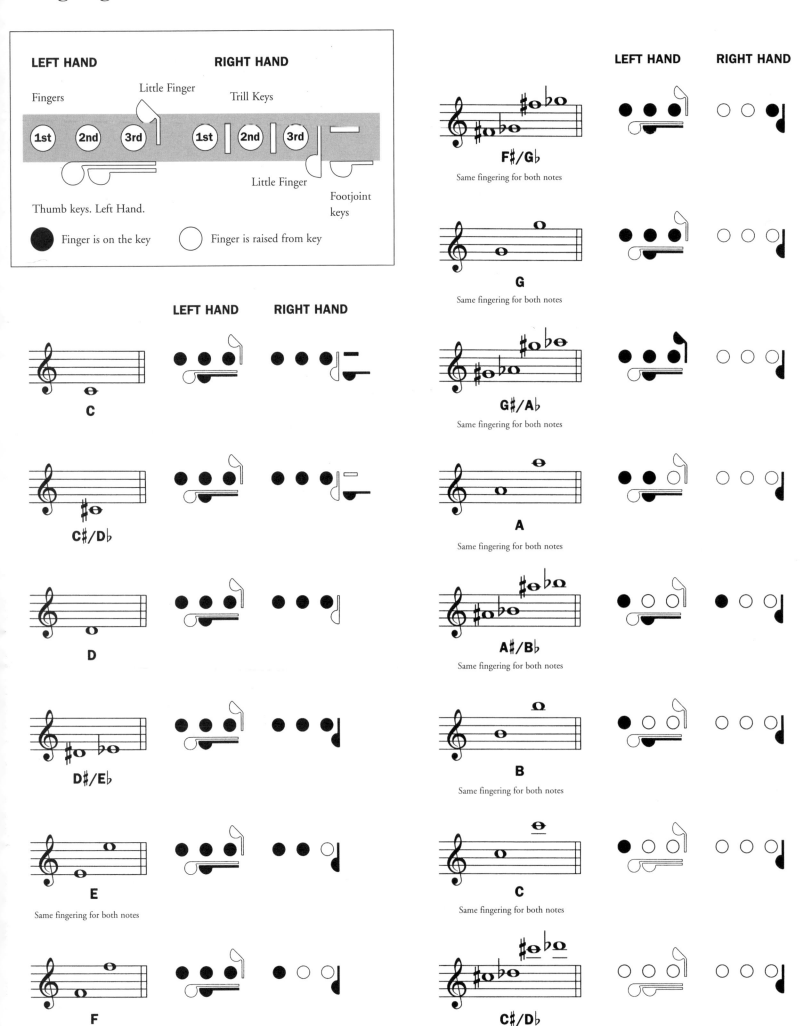

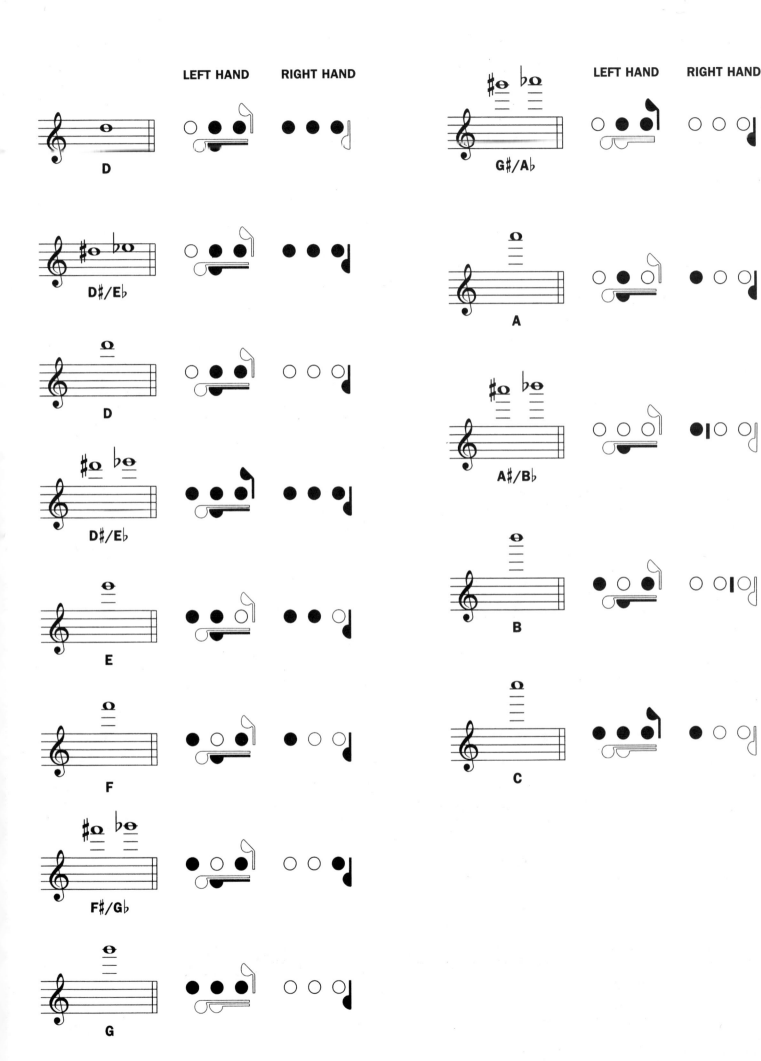

A Whiter Shade Of Pale

Words & Music by Keith Reid & Gary Brooker

A Whole New World

(From Walt Disney Pictures' "Aladdin")

Words by Tim Rice
Music by Alan Menken

Medium tempo (♩ = 110)

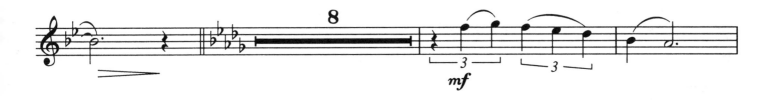

Bridge Over Troubled Water

Words & Music by Paul Simon

He Ain't Heavy... He's My Brother

Words by Bob Russell
Music by Bobby Scott

Rather slow

Here, There And Everywhere

Words & Music by John Lennon & Paul McCartney

Moderately Slow

Don't Cry For Me Argentina

Music by Andrew Lloyd Webber
Words by Tim Rice

mp

mf   *molto*

I Know Him So Well

Words & Music by Benny Andersson, Tim Rice & Björn Ulvaeus

Medium slow ($\downarrow$ = 70)

dim.   mp

I Dreamed A Dream

Words by Herbert Kretzmer
Music by Claude-Michel Schönberg
Original Text by Alain Boublil & Jean-Marc Natel

Slow (♩ = c. 64)

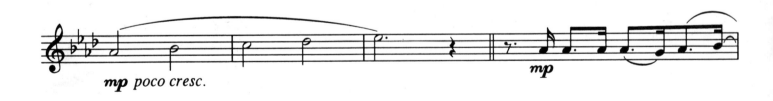

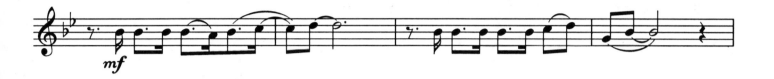

Imagine

Words & Music by John Lennon

Medium slow (♩ = 76)

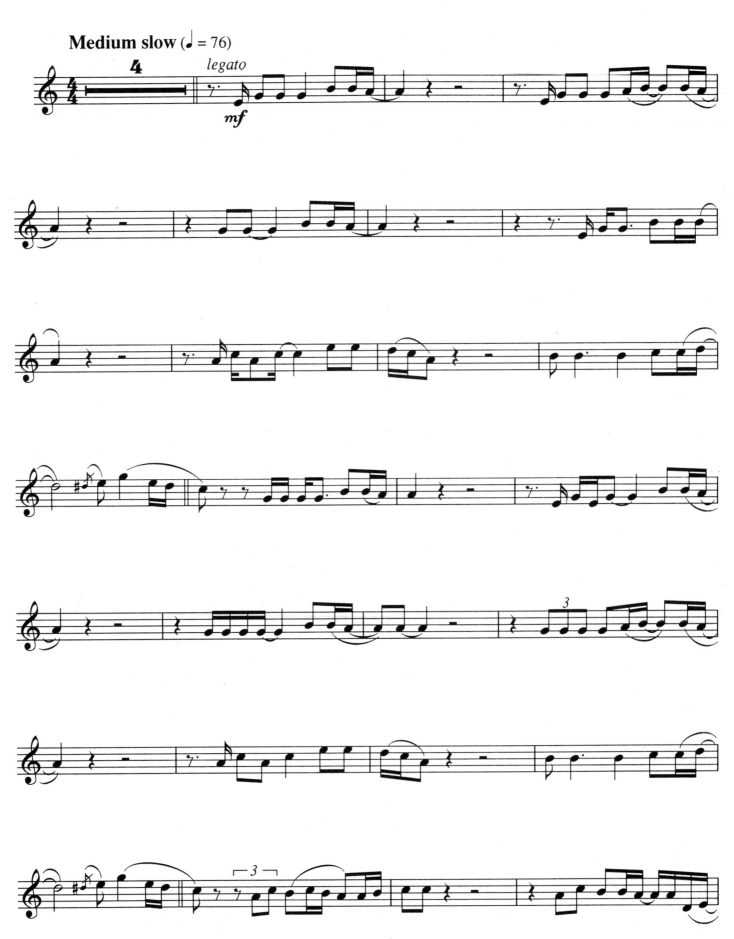

Optional 8ve to end

rall.
loco

Lady Madonna

Words & Music by John Lennon & Paul McCartney

Rhythmically

32

Moon River

Words by Johnny Mercer
Music by Henry Mancini

Medium slow (♩ = 84)

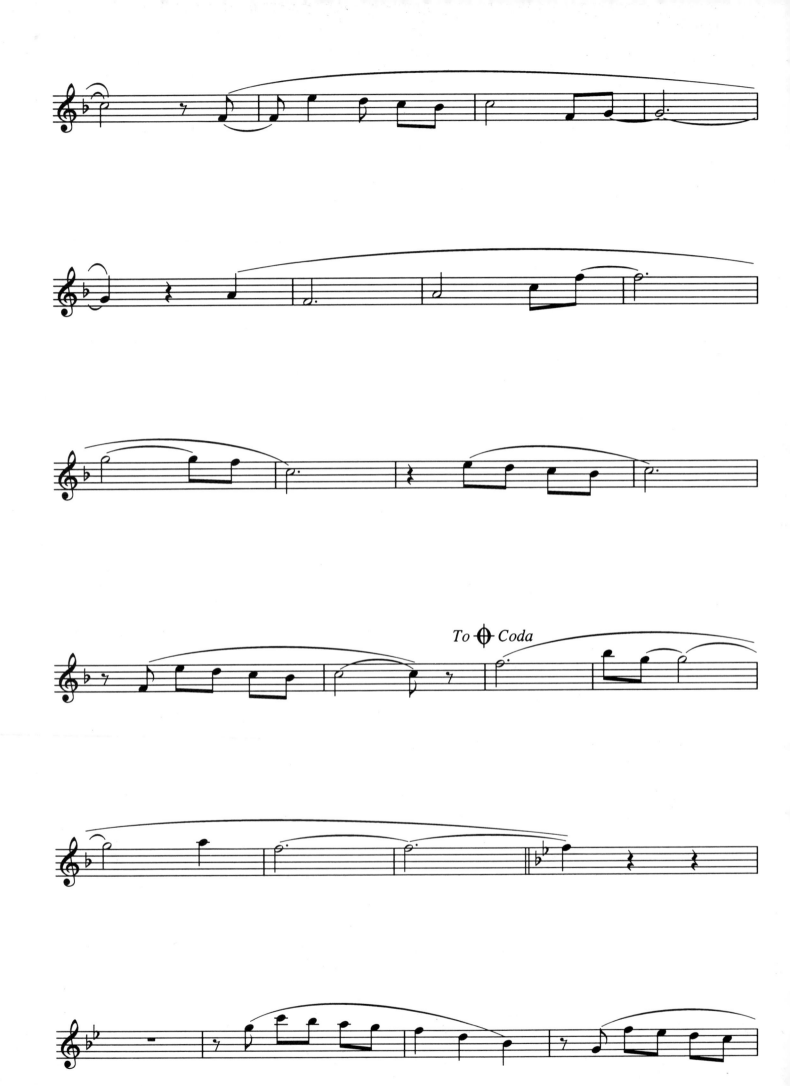

To ⊕ Coda

D. %: al Coda

CODA

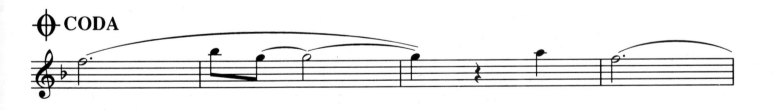

rall.

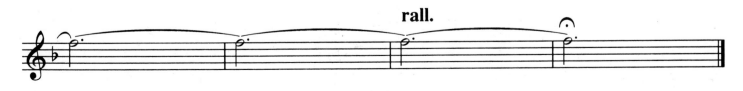

Nights In White Satin

Words & Music by Justin Hayward

D. 𝄋 al Coda

🜉 CODA

She Loves You

Words & Music by John Lennon & Paul McCartney

Bright Tempo

40

Mull Of Kintyre

Words & Music by Paul McCartney & Denny Laine

Unchained Melody

Words by Hy Zaret
Music by Alex North

molto rall.

Up Where We Belong

Words & Music by Jack Nitzsche, Will Jennings & Buffy Sainte-Marie

Medium slow ♩ = 70

Where Do I Begin

(Theme from Love Story)

Words by Carl Sigman
Music by Francis Lai

Medium slow (♩ = 76)

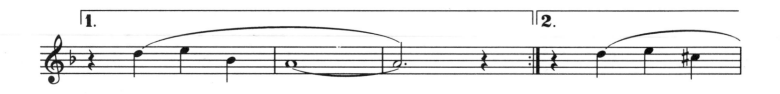

D.%. al Coda

CODA

Yesterday

Words & Music by John Lennon & Paul McCartney

Moderately

espress.

You Must Love Me

Music by Andrew Lloyd Webber
Lyrics by Tim Rice

Words

Words & Music by Barry Gibb, Robin Gibb & Maurice Gibb

Moderately

Printed in Malta by Interprint Limited

11/03 (49311)